Written by Nick Page
Illustrated by Tim Hutchinson
Designed by Jane Horne

Copyright © 2011 make believe ideas ltd
The Wilderness, Berkhamsted, Herts, HP4 2AZ.
565 Royal Parkway, Nashville, TN 37214, USA.
Text copyright © 2011 Nick Page

THE FURRY FREEDOM FIGHTERS

THE DAWN OF THE RED FANG

THE ROBOT OF DR. KLAWS

TWO BOOKS IN ONE!

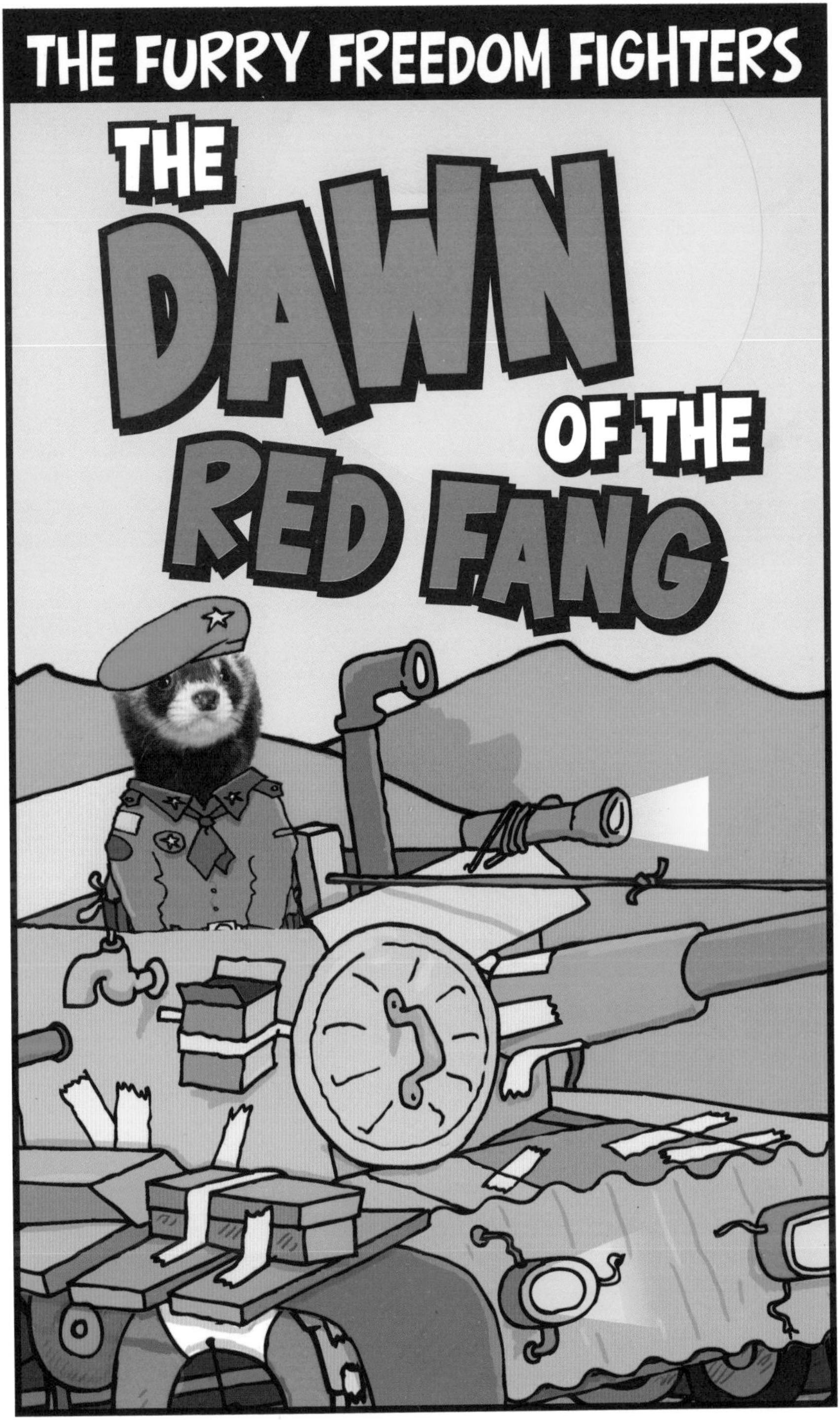
THE FURRY FREEDOM FIGHTERS
THE DAWN OF THE RED FANG

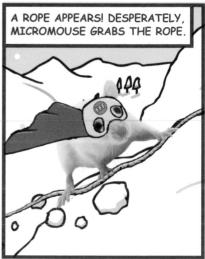

SO THE MEERKAT ARMY STARTS TO MOVE TOWARDS THE DOORS OF THE PETSHOPOLIS BANK!

I DON'T LIKE THIS!

WE'VE GOT NO CHOICE!

WHAT WOULD BERNARD SAY?

WAIT A MINUTE. I DIDN'T KNOW THIS TANK COULD FLY . .

YES! YOU **WILL** DO AS I SAY, OR YOU WILL FACE MY FLYING TANK!

ARGH! WHAT ARE YOU DOING? WELL, IT DOESN'T MATTER; MY ARMY WILL RESCUE ME!

DO YOU NEED A LIFT?

BUT THEN...

POOF!

SUDDENLY, THE DOOR TO THE BANK DISAPPEARS!

WHERE DID THE DOOR GO? WHAT'S HAPPENED TO MY ARMY?

THE SHOCKING ORIGIN OF

SUPERHAMMY!

HAMMY DOESN'T REALISE THAT HIS OWNER, TIMMY THOMPSON, IS THE SON OF THE FAMOUS SCIENTIST, THOMAS THOMPSON. ONE DAY, IN MR THOMPSON'S LABORATORY...

PONG!

POO!

WHAT A MESS! THESE VEGETABLES LOOK ROTTEN. YUCK!

LATER ON...

DARLING, WHERE ARE THE VEGETABLES THAT WERE IN MY LAB?

WELL, THEY LOOKED A BIT ROTTEN, DARLING, SO I TOOK THEM AWAY.

BUT...BUT... THEY WERE MY NEW EXPERIMENT: VEGETABLES THAT GIVE YOU SUPERHUMAN STRENGTH!

OH, NO! I GAVE THEM TO THE HAMSTER!

THE FAMILY RUSHES TO HAMMY'S CAGE.

I'M SORRY, SON. THERE'S NOTHING WE CAN DO. I DON'T THINK ANY ANIMAL COULD SURVIVE THAT SORT OF SUPER-VEGETABLE POWER!

OH, NO! POOR HAMMY!

WHAT'S THIS? AS NIGHT FALLS, SOMETHING STRANGE BEGINS TO HAPPEN...

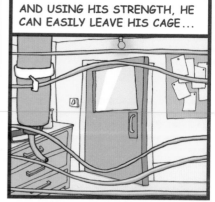

MEANWHILE, SOMEONE HAS BEEN WATCHING HAMMY.

A SUPER-POWERED HAMSTER! AMAZING! HOW WOULD YOU LIKE TO JOIN THE NEW SUPER-TEAM I'M FORMING?

I'D LOVE TO!

YOU'LL NEED A COSTUME THOUGH — AN ORDINARY HAMSTER FLYING AROUND WILL JUST LOOK SILLY.

AND SO, SUPERHAMMY JOINED THE FURRY FREEDOM FIGHTERS. TO HIS OWNERS, HE IS STILL JUST HAMMY...

FFF

BUT WHEN DANGER CALLS, WHEN SOMEONE IS IN TROUBLE, OR WHEN THERE'S A CHANCE OF SOME FREE PEANUTS, HE BECOMES SUPERHAMMY: THE MOST POWERFUL HAMSTER ON EARTH!

THE END . . .
(NEARLY)

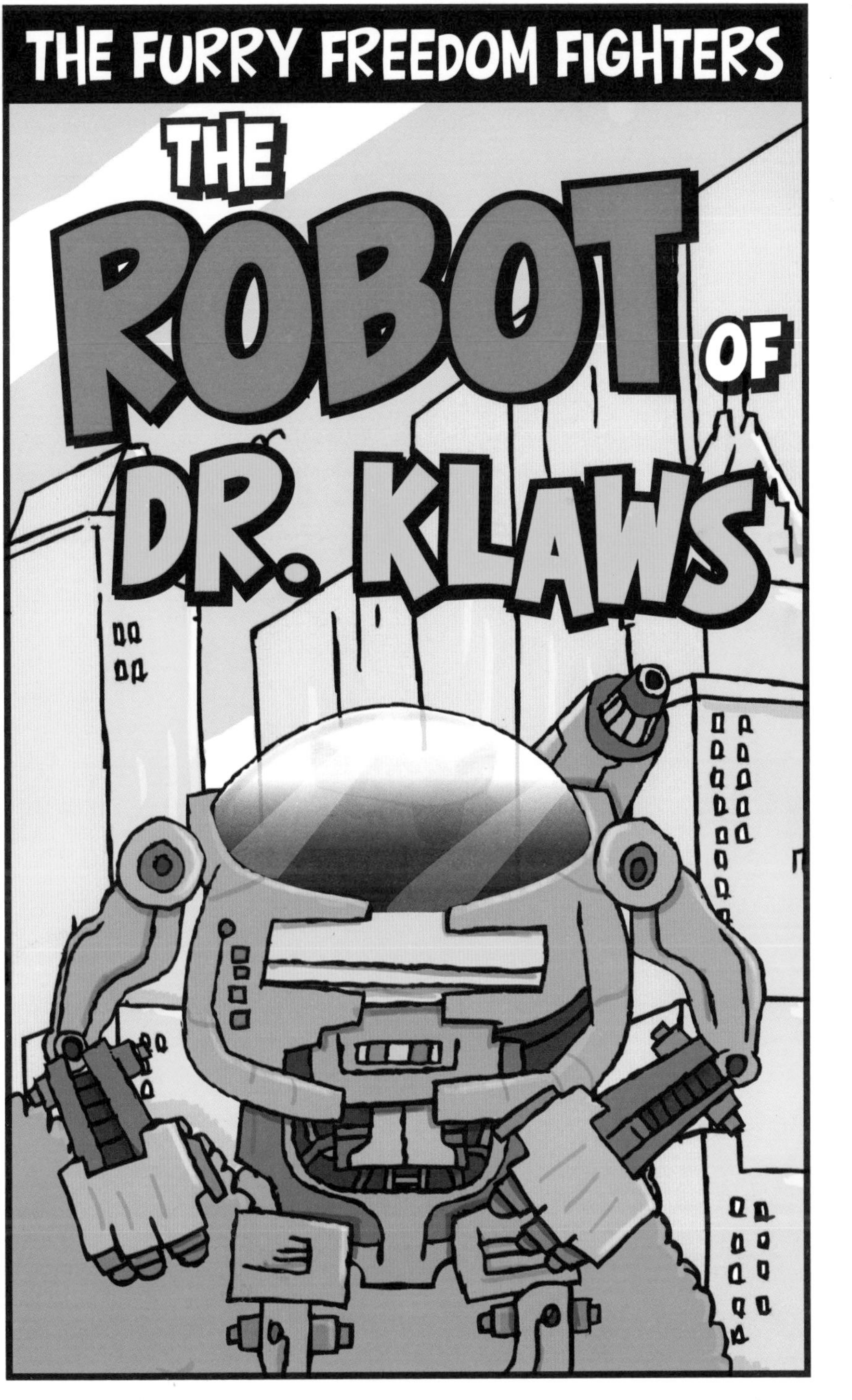
THE FURRY FREEDOM FIGHTERS
THE ROBOT OF DR. KLAWS

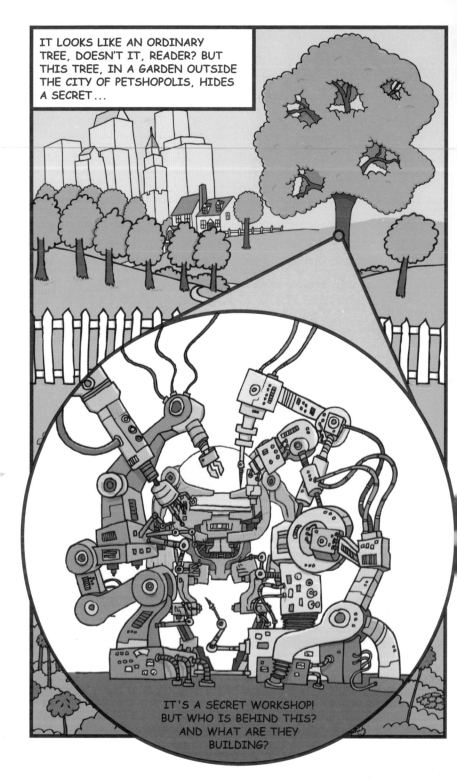

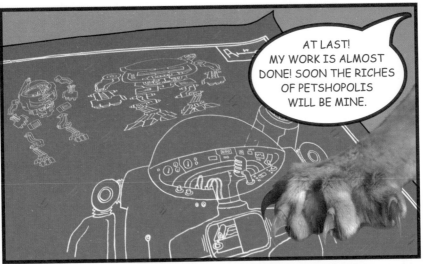

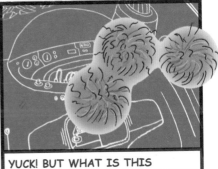

*LOOK OUT FOR THESE CATS AGAIN IN
THE FURRY FREEDOM FIGHTERS: ALL HAIL THE JELLYFIEND.

THEN...

EEWWW! WHAT HAVE YOU BEEN EATING?

IT'S A SMOKESCREEN! IT WILL COVER YOUR ATTACK!

BUT THIS WON'T STOP DR. KLAWS!

HA! MY FANS CAN BLOW YOUR SMOKE AWAY.

LOOK OUT! I CAN'T STOP MYSELF!

SQUAWK!

OH, NO! THE FAN HAS BLOWN SUPERHAMMY THROUGH THE AIR AND STRAIGHT INTO BIRDBRAIN!

MEANWHILE, MICROMOUSE HAS SPOTTED DR. KLAWS AND DECIDES THAT HE MUST RETURN TO HELP HIS FRIENDS. WHEN...

STOP!

KEEP AWAY! YOU CAN'T GO THERE!

BUT MICROMOUSE CAN GO ANYWHERE, USING HIS INCREDIBLE SHRINKING POWERS!

ZAP!

THEY CAN'T STOP ME IF THEY CAN'T SEE ME!

MICROMOUSE RUNS THROUGH THE CROWD TO HELP HIS FRIENDS!

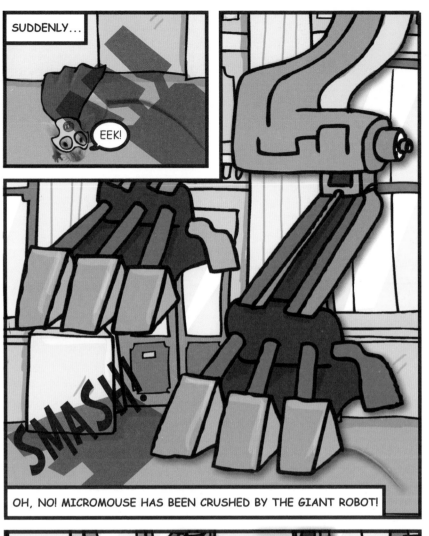

OH, NO! MICROMOUSE HAS BEEN CRUSHED BY THE GIANT ROBOT!

BUT WAIT!

GROAN! WHAT HAS HAPPENED TO ME!

BLINK! BLINK!

I'M...I'M, STILL ALIVE!

YES, READER, MICROMOUSE IS STILL ALIVE! THERE WAS A SMALL HOLE IN THE BOTTOM OF THE ROBOT'S FOOT, AND OUR TINY HERO CRAWLED THROUGH IT AND INTO THE ROBOT.

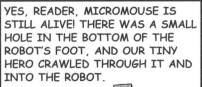

HOLE IN THE BOTTOM OF THE ROBOT'S FOOT.

INSIDE THE ROBOT:

OH, I'M SO TINY, WHAT CAN I DO? THIS IS SUCH A BIG ROBOT, AND IT IS CONTROLLED BY A CAT!

BE BRAVE, MICROMOUSE! NEVER GIVE UP! NO MATTER HOW SMALL YOU ARE, YOU CAN ALWAYS MAKE A DIFFERENCE!

THE BRAVE LITTLE MOUSE STARTS TO RUN.

I MUST BE CAREFUL.

BUT THEN!

HE'S ESCAPING! QUICK! WE MUST STOP HIM!

STOP HIM!

THEY'VE SPOTTED ME!

RUN, LITTLE MOUSE, RUN!

THE SCIENTISTS TRY TO STOP HIM.

MISSED ME! BUT THAT WAS CLOSE!

THE OTHER MICE CHEER HIM ON!

YAY!

YOU CAN DO IT!

WHO'S THE **FASTEST?** WHO'S THE **STRONGEST?**

WHO'S THE MOST **EVIL?**

FIND OUT MORE ABOUT
THE FURRY FREEDOM FIGHTERS
AND THEIR FEARSOME FOES!

BIRDBRAIN

BIRDBRAIN COMES FROM THE MYSTERIOUS KINGDOM OF THE BIRDS. NOT JUST A FAMOUS INVENTOR, HE IS ALSO THE BRAINS BEHIND THE FURRY FREEDOM FIGHTERS.

REAL NAME: TOO HARD TO PRONOUNCE!

BRAINS: ★★★★★

STRENGTH: ★

SPEED: ★★

WEAPONS: ★★★

SURPRISE: ★★★

WEAKNESS: HE MAY BE BRAINY, BUT HE'S JUST A BIRD, SO HE CAN BE OVERPOWERED BY STRONG ENEMIES.

MICROMOUSE

WHILE ESCAPING FROM A SECRET LABORATORY, MICROMOUSE WAS HIT BY A SHRINKING RAY, GIVING HIM THE ABILITY TO TURN SUPER-SMALL AND GO SUPER-FAST!

REAL NAME: UNKNOWN

BRAINS: ★★

STRENGTH: ★

SPEED: ★★★★★

WEAPONS: ★

SURPRISE: ★★★★★

WEAKNESS: CHEESE — HE CAN'T RESIST IT! AND WHEN HE IS MICRO-SIZE, HE ALWAYS RUNS THE RISK OF BEING STEPPED ON.

TURBO TORTOISE

SECRET GOVERNMENT AGENT, TERRY TORTOISE, WAS TURNED INTO A WALKING TIME BOMB BY THE EVIL SQUIRREL, DR. NUTTY!

REAL NAME: TERRY TORTOISE

BRAINS: ★★★

STRENGTH: ★★★★★

SPEED: ★★★★

WEAPONS: ★★★★★

SURPRISE: ★★★

WEAKNESS: BEING TIPPIED OVER! LIKE ALL TORTOISES, IF YOU TIP HIM OVER, HE HAS PROBLEMS GETTING UP AGAIN!

SUPERHAMMY

SUPERHAMMY IS THE SUPER-POWERED HAMSTER.
HE CAN FLY THROUGH THE AIR, HE CAN TEAR UP WHOLE
TREES — WHAT MORE COULD YOU WANT FROM A HAMSTER?

REAL NAME: HAMMY THE HAMSTER

BRAINS: ★★★

STRENGTH: ★★★★★

SPEED: ★★★★

WEAPONS: ★

SURPRISE: ★★

WEAKNESS: BEING A HAMSTER, SUPERHAMMY'S
BIGGEST CHALLENGE IS STAYING
AWAKE DURING THE DAY!

DR. KLAWS

THIS PEDIGREE CAT IS A FIENDISH INVENTOR.
HE TRIED TO DEFEAT THE FURRY FREEDOM
FIGHTERS BY BUILDING A ROBOT.

REAL NAME: PRINCE TIDDLES DE CREAMPUFF III

BRAINS: ★★★★★

STRENGTH: ★

SPEED: ★★

WEAPONS: ★★★★★

SURPRISE: ★★★

WEAKNESS: FURBALLS — LIKE ALL CATS, HE JUST
CAN'T STOP COUGHING THEM UP.

THE RED FANG

THIS MAD MANIAC TURNED THE HUNGRY
MEERKATS INTO AN ARMY AND THEN MARCHED
THEM INTO PETSHOPOLIS!

REAL NAME: ERICH VON STOATWEASEL

BRAINS: ★★★★

STRENGTH: ★

SPEED: ★★

WEAPONS: ★★★★★

SURPRISE: ★★★★

WEAKNESS: HIS OWN BIG HEAD! HE THINKS
THAT HE CAN NEVER BE DEFEATED,
BUT THAT'S WHERE HE IS WRONG!

THE MEERKAT ARMY

THE MEERKATS WERE PERSUADED TO ATTACK PETSHOPOLIS BY THE RED FANG, BUT ALL THEY WANTED WAS SOMETHING TO EAT.

REAL NAME: TOO MANY TO MENTION

BRAINS: ★

STRENGTH: ★★

SPEED: ★★

WEAPONS: ★

SURPRISE: ★★

WEAKNESS: THEY ARE NOT THE SMARTEST OF ANIMALS!

MORE AMAZING ADVENTURES FROM THE FURRY FREEDOM FIGHTERS: